The Unofficial Devilishly Difficult

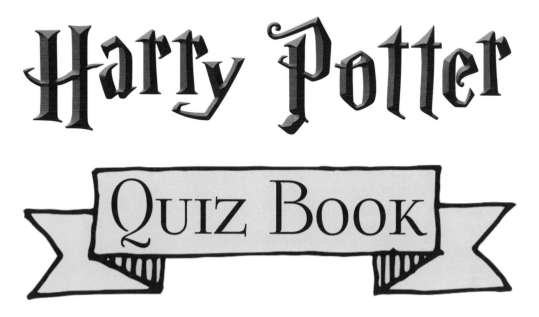

Harry Potter

Quiz Book

From potions to professors, spirits to spells & witches to wizards... this devilishly demanding quiz book will discover just how much you really know about the wizarding world of Harry Potter

D0317260

THE UNOFFICIAL DEVILISHLY DIFFICULT Harry Potter QUIZ BOOK

From potions to professors, spirits to spells & witches to wizards... this devilishly demanding quiz book will discover just how much you really know about the wizarding world of Harry Potter.

ISBN 978-1-912511-60-0

DISCLAIMER

Contents

Harry Potter Quiz Book

Enemies of hard questions beware. This devilishly fiendish quiz book contains a complete examination of the Wizarding World of Harry Potter. If you haven't read the books and have only seen the movies, you might need some Felix Felicis to navigate your way through.

From potions to professors, ghosts to spells, and wands to witches, discover just how much you know. Can you achieve a result worthy of Hermione Granger? Good luck!

Hogwarts - A History

Hogwarts is home to the British school of Witchcraft and Wizardry and is an ancient castle located somewhere in Scotland. It stands in grounds with the Black Lake and the Forbidden Forest and is magnificent, with towers, cloisters, and marvellous magical rooms. When it comes to all things Hogwarts are you as wise as Dumbledore or as daft as a troll?

1. Featuring in a number of key episodes including being used as a place to hide Harry's Potions textbook, the place for Dumbledore's Army to learn defence against the dark arts from Harry, and a key scene in the Battle for Hogwarts, what is the name of the special room on the 7th floor of Hogwarts Castle?

a. The Room of Requirement
b. The Room That Appears When You Need It
c. The Magic Hidden Room

2. They move. They are hung with moving pictures. One even has a false step that Harry falls through and is nearly caught out of bed by Professor Snape in The Goblet of Fire. We're talking about the Hogwarts staircases. How many are there?

a. 92
b. 302
c. 142

3. It is not possible to apparate in and out of Hogwarts Castle due to the anti-disapparation jinx, so how did the Death Eaters gain access to the Astronomy tower the night that Dumbledore was killed?

a. The school caretaker opened the main door for them
b. Draco Malfoy fixed a vanishing cabinet that had a twin in Borgin and Burkes
c. The Death Eaters drank a vanishing potion

4. Each house has its own dedicated area within Hogwarts. Ravenclaw students have to answer a riddle to gain entry to their common room but to get inside Gryffindor Tower, there is a password. What is the first ever Gryffindor password in Harry's time at Hogwarts?

a. Fat Lady
b. Caput Draconis
c. Mimbus Mimbletonia

5. In *The Prisoner of Azkaban*, Fred and George Weasley present Harry with The Marauders Map. There are seven secret passages detailed on the map. Which is the one Harry uses first?

a. The One-Eyed Witch passage to Honeyduke's in Hogsmeade
b. The Gregory The Smarmy passage on the 5th floor corridor
c. The Hogs Head Pub passage

6. Harry found out on his 11th birthday that he was a wizard and had a place at Hogwarts School of Witchcraft and Wizardry. What is the name of the muggle school Harry had been planning to attend'?

a. Smeltings Academy
b. Stonewall High School
c. Little Whingeing Comprehensive

7. The kitchens at Hogwarts are manned by an army of house elf servants. Fred and George found the entrance and shared the secret with Harry, Ron, and Hermione. Which fruit do you have to tickle on the painting to make the door open?

a. Apple
b. Banana
c. Pear

8. The first years are taken from the Hogwarts Express to the castle by boats across the lake. Students from other years are taken in carriages drawn by thestrals. To most of the students, thestrals are invisible. Why can some people see them?

a. They wear glasses
b. They have seen death
c. They subscribe to *The Quibbler*

9. The entrance to the Chamber of Secrets is in Moaning Myrtle's bathroom. Myrtle lives there because she died after seeing the basilisk. In which year was the Chamber of Secrets first opened?

a. 1983
b. 1963
c. 1943

10. The first magical person Harry meets after he is left at Number 4 Privet Drive with the Dursleys is Hagrid. When Harry asks him who he is, what does Hagrid say his job is?

a. Head Lumberjack in the Forbidden Forest
b. Professor of Magical Creatures
c. Keeper of Grounds and Keys at Hogwarts

11. Hogwarts Castle has been standing for more than 1,000 years. It has four houses named after the four founders of Hogwarts School of Witchcraft and Wizardry: Gryffindor, Hufflepuff, Ravenclaw, and Slytherin. What is the first name of the witch Hufflepuff?

a. Hermione
b. Hepzibah
c. Helga

12. Hogwarts Castle is enchanted to be invisible to muggles. Should they venture close enough, what is written on the warning sign?

a. Danger, do not enter, unsafe.
b. Stop! No muggles allowed
c. Warning. Magical creatures ahead.

13. The school has many enchantments and protective spells, some of which were broken by Voldemort and the Death Eaters during the Battle for Hogwarts. What is the spell that professor McGonagall uses to get the stone soldier statues to defend the castle?

a. Motivus locomotivus
b. Piertotum locomotor
c. Statutus motoloco

14. Harry was helped by Cedric Diggory to solve the second clue in the Triwizard Tournament. Cedric gave him the password to the prefects' bathroom where Harry took a soak in a pool-sized bath filled by water and bubbles of all different colours. On which floor will you find the bathroom?

a. 3rd floor
b. 4th floor
c. 5th floor

15. Every good school has a song and motto. The Hogwarts school song has words but no tune. You just sing it to any tune you like. The motto however, is in Latin and set in stone. What is it?

a. Hon y soit qui mal y pense
b. Draco dormiens nunquam titillandus
c. Ex spes fortitudo

8

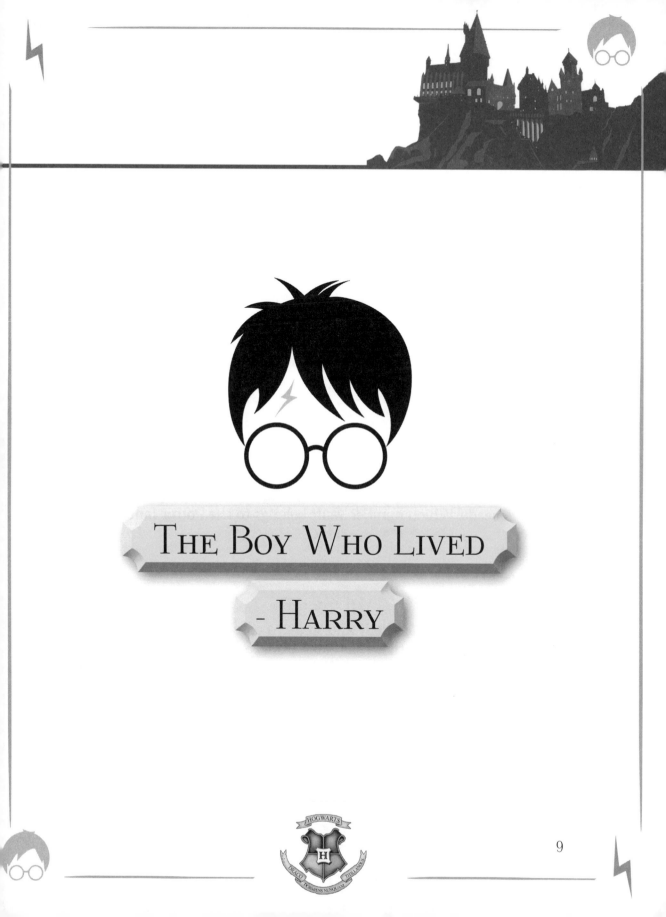

THE BOY WHO LIVED

- HARRY

1. Harry's parents were killed by Lord Voldemort because Peter Pettigrew told him the address. Because Pettigrew was the "secret keeper", this act broke the enchantment that protected the Potters house. What was that enchantment?

a. Protego
b. Fidelius charm
c. Screening charm

2. Before Uncle Vernon and Aunt Petunia allowed Harry to move into Dudley's extra bedroom, he slept in a cupboard under the stairs. What toy did he play with in the cupboard?

a. Toy soldiers
b. Yo-yo
c. A games console

3. Harry's parents left him a pile of gold that was in safekeeping at Gringotts Bank in Hogsmeade. Which number vault belongs to the Potter family?

a. 627
b. 687
c. 654

4. Harry's wand is made from holly and shares a core with Voldemort's wand. They both contain a tail feather that came from Fawkes, the phoenix owned by Dumbledore. How long is Harry's wand?

a. 12 inches
b. 11 inches
c. 10 inches

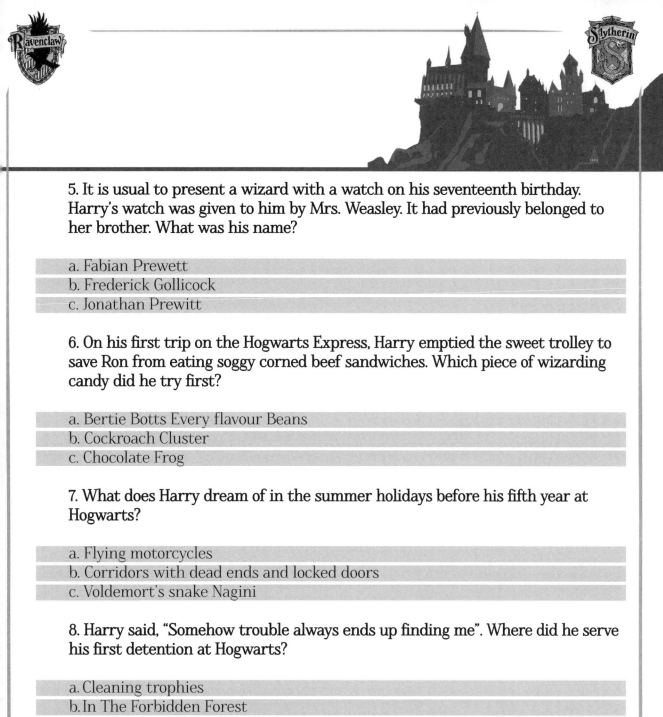

5. It is usual to present a wizard with a watch on his seventeenth birthday. Harry's watch was given to him by Mrs. Weasley. It had previously belonged to her brother. What was his name?

a. Fabian Prewett

b. Frederick Gollicock

c. Jonathan Prewitt

6. On his first trip on the Hogwarts Express, Harry emptied the sweet trolley to save Ron from eating soggy corned beef sandwiches. Which piece of wizarding candy did he try first?

a. Bertie Botts Every flavour Beans

b. Cockroach Cluster

c. Chocolate Frog

7. What does Harry dream of in the summer holidays before his fifth year at Hogwarts?

a. Flying motorcycles

b. Corridors with dead ends and locked doors

c. Voldemort's snake Nagini

8. Harry said, "Somehow trouble always ends up finding me". Where did he serve his first detention at Hogwarts?

a. Cleaning trophies

b. In The Forbidden Forest

c. Signing autographs

9. Harry had his first experience with Dementors in *The Prisoner of Azkaban* and asked Professor Remus Lupin to teach him the Patronus charm. Where did Lupin find the Boggart in Hogwarts Castle he used in lieu of a Dementor?

a. The Kitchens
b. Teacher's Staff Room
c. Snape's Office

10. In his fifth year, Harry attended special one-on-one lessons with Professor Snape. Despite telling Draco that Harry was attending remedial potions, what was Snape teaching Harry?

a. Arithmancy
b. Legilimency
c. Occlumency

11. Hermione achieved 12 OWLs. Harry passed 7 of the 9 he sat. Which two did he fail?

a. History of Magic and Divination
b. Divination and Potions
c. Potions and Magic History

12. When Harry has the Elder Wand, he uses it to cast just one spell. Which spell?

a. Expelliarmis
b. Diffindo
c. Reparo

13. Harry learned to fly on a school broomstick but then was gifted a Nimbus 2000 by Professor McGonagall. After it was broken, when Harry had a fall brought on by seeing a dementor in a quidditch match, Sirius sent him a new broom. Which model was it?

a. Comet
b. Firebolt
c. Nimbus 2001

14. Harry was presented with 1,000 galleons for winning the Triwizard Tournament. What did he do with the money?

a. Gave it to Fred and George
b. Donated it to St. Mungo's Hospital for Magical Maladies and Injuries
c. Bought a new broomstick.

15. Which of the three Peverell Brothers was the original owner of the invisibility cloak and from whom it is believed Harry descended?

a. Cadmus
b. Antioch
c. Ignotus

THE BRIGHTEST WITCH OF HER AGE

- HERMIONE

Bookish, brainy, and beautiful, Hermione Granger is the level-headed girl who keeps Harry and Ron grounded. She is exceedingly bright and compassionate towards all living things.

1. What is the occupation of Hermione's parents. (Professor Slughorn asks the question during one of his dinner parties?) Are they...

a. Doctors
b. Dentists
c. Dog walkers

2. Hermione is recognised as being very intelligent. Which house did the Sorting Hat consider putting Hermione in before it chose Gryffindor?

a. Hufflepuff
b. Ravenclaw
c. Slytherin

3. When Harry, Ron, and Hermione were caught by a gang of snatchers when looking for the horcruxes, they gave false names. Which name did Hermione use?

a. Susan Bones
b. Pansy Parkinson
c. Penelope Clearwater

4. Hermione discovered the recipe for Polyjuice potion in *Moste Potente Potions*. What is the missing ingredient from this list - Lacewing flies, leeches, powdered Bicorn horn, knotgrass, fluxweed, shredded Boomslang skin, and

a. A bit of the person you want to turn into
b. Aconite
c. Dragon's blood

5. In *The Chamber of Secrets*, Hermione had solved the riddle of what was the monster but was petrified before she could let anyone know. Where was she petrified?

a. Outside the girls bathroom
b. Outside the library
c. Outside the Defence Against the Dark Arts classroom

6. The love potion Amortentia smells different to each person according to the aromas they find most attractive. What did it smell like to Hermione?

a. Freshly baked croissants, new books, and peppermint chewing gum
b. Freshly mown grass, new parchment, and spearmint toothpaste
c. Freshly painted walls, new carpet, and mint humbugs

7. In the defence against the dark arts lesson with Professor Lupin, what form did Hermione's boggart take?

a. Voldemort killing her family
b. A giant cobra
c. Professor McGonagall telling her she'd failed her exams

8. Forever humane, in her fourth year at Hogwarts, Hermione founded an organisation. What was it?

a. Witches for Equal Rights
b. Society for Promotion of Elfish Welfare
c. Wizards Against the Dark Arts

9. During the Triwizard Tournament, Hermione started to receive hate mail after an article about her and Harry in *The Daily Prophet* by Rita Skeeter. What did her hand get covered in when she opened one letter?

a. Bubotuber pus
b. Stinksap
c. Salamander droppings

10. In year three, Hermione took extra lessons thanks to a time turner. Which elective class did Hermione study with Professor Bathsheda Babbling?

a. Arithmancy
b. The Study of Ancient Runes
c. Muggle Studies

11. Hermione achieved ten OWLs. For nine, she was marked as Outstanding. For which subject did she only receive Exceeds Expectations?

a. Herbology
b. Defence Against the Dark Arts
c. Potions

12. In *The Order of the Phoenix* when Dumbledore's Army were fighting with Voldemort's supporters in the Ministry of Magic, which Death Eater injured Hermione?

a. Bellatrix Lestrange
b. Avery
c. Antonin Dolohov

13. Hermione marries Ron Weasley and 19 years after the death of Lord Voldermort. We know they have two children, but what are their names?

a. Lily and Theodore
b. Rose and Hugo
c. Harry and Ginny

14. Before going on the quest for horcruxes with Harry and Ron, Hermione used the obliviate charm to wipe her parents' memories of her. What new name did she give them?

a. Wendell and Monica Wilkins
b. James and Lily Watkins
c. Harold and Molly Wentworth

15. In order to carry all the stuff they needed to search for horcruxes, Hermione charmed a small beaded bag so that it had limitless space. What was the charm she used?

a. A hold-all charm
b. An undetectable extension charm
c. A no-bottom charm

Harry's Best Friend

- Ron

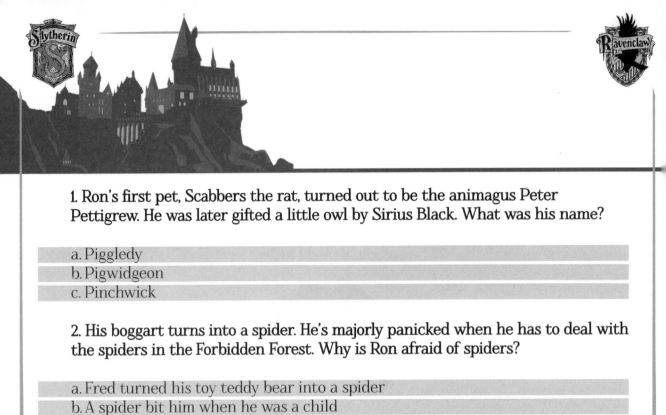

1. Ron's first pet, Scabbers the rat, turned out to be the animagus Peter Pettigrew. He was later gifted a little owl by Sirius Black. What was his name?

a. Piggledy
b. Pigwidgeon
c. Pinchwick

2. His boggart turns into a spider. He's majorly panicked when he has to deal with the spiders in the Forbidden Forest. Why is Ron afraid of spiders?

a. Fred turned his toy teddy bear into a spider
b. A spider bit him when he was a child
c. Charlie turned into a spider to scare him

3. As a reward for being made a prefect in his sixth year, Ron asked for a new broom. Which model did he receive?

a. Cleansweep 11
b. Comet 260
c. Starshooter 5,000

4. Which of these is a quote from Hermione about Ron?

a. You have the emotional range of a teaspoon
b. You are as stupid as a troll
c. You'll never be as good as Harry

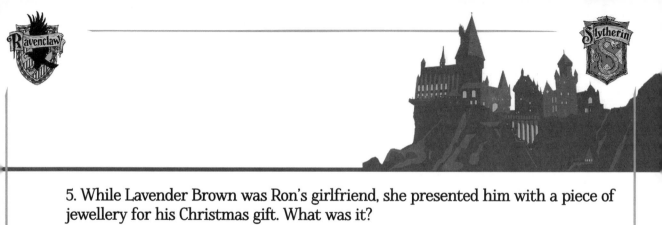

5. While Lavender Brown was Ron's girlfriend, she presented him with a piece of jewellery for his Christmas gift. What was it?

a. A bracelet inscribed with the words Won, Won
b. A gold chain suspended with letters spelling sweetheart
c. A heart-shaped locket with her picture inside

6. The Mirror of Erised shows what your heart most desires. Harry saw his parents. What did Ron see?

a. Himself holding lots of money
b. Himself kissing Hermione
c. Himself holding the Hogwarts Quidditch Cup

7. Ron's middle name is also the name of one of his uncles. Which one?

a. Gideon Prewett
b. Bilius Weasley
c. Fabian Prewett

8. The Slytherins made up a song about Ron to put him off his game when he was made keeper for the Gryffindor team. According to the lyrics of "Weasley is Our King" where was he born?

a. In a bin
b. In a dump
c. In the zoo

9. When Harry, Ron and Hermione took Polyjuice potion in their second year, which of the Slytherin students did Ron turn into?

a. Gregory Goyle
b. Blaize Zabini
c. Vincent Crabbe

10. When Harry and Ron met on the Hogwarts Express, Ron told Harry about his collection of chocolate frog cards. Which two cards did Ron still need?

a. Merlin and Agrippa
b. Ptolemy and Agrippa
c. Nicholas Flamel and Merlin

11. Ron attempted to curse Draco Malfoy when he called Hermione a mudblood. What happened as a result?

a. He sicked up slugs for an hour
b. He blew bubbles through his nose for the rest of the day
c. Malfoy was affected by the body bind curse.

12. One of the protections of the philosopher's stone was a chess game. In the "greatest game of chess that Hogwarts has ever seen" which piece did Ron take the place of?

a. King
b. Bishop
c. Knight

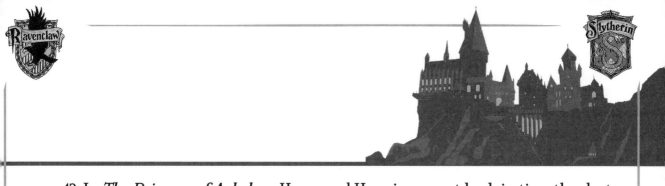

13. In *The Prisoner of Azkaban*, Harry and Hermione went back in time thanks to Hermione's Time Turner. Why didn't Ron accompany them?

a. It was the Christmas holidays and he had gone to Romania to visit Charlie
b. He was in hospital with a broken leg
c. He had fallen out with Harry.

14. What does Ron hate most about himself?

a. Being poor
b. His red hair
c. Not being as good at quidditch as his brother Charlie

15. On which birthday did Ron give Harry a pocket sneakoscope, an instrument that gives a warning signal when someone untrustworthy is detected nearby?

a. 15th
b. 16th
c. 17th

THE GREATEST WIZARD EVER

- ALBUS DUMBLEDORE

Albus Dumbledore was old (age unknown) and rather eccentric. He was a father figure to Harry and much beloved by the staff and students of Hogwarts.

1. Acknowledged as the best Headmaster Hogwarts has ever had, what was Dumbledore's position at the school before he was appointed to the headship?

a. Professor of Transfiguration

b. Charms Professor

c. Professor of Care of Magical Creatures

2. Although we never got to see it, Dumbledore had a scar above his left knee. What was it shaped like?

a. A phoenix

b. A map of the London Underground

c. A dragon

3. What was the name of the wizard that Dumbledore struck up a close friendship with after he had to stay home to look after his sick sister?

a. Newt Scamander

b. Cornelius Fudge

c. Gellert Grindlewald

4. Every witch and wizard has a patronus. Albus Dumbledore's patronus took the form of a phoenix. What form did the patronus of his brother Aberforth take?

a. Stag

b. Goat

c. Ram

5. Albus Dumbledore had a sweet tooth but he was not very fond of Bertie Bott's Every Flavour Beans because he once ate which flavour?

a. Earwax
b. Tripe
c. Vomit

6. When he graduated from Hogwarts, Dumbledore had planned a trip around Europe with Elphias Doge, his loyal friend. According to "The Life and Lies of Albus Dumbledore" by Rita Skeeter, what was his nickname?

a. Dogbreath
b. Dodgy
c. Poxface

7. When Cornelius Fudge arrived at Hogwarts to arrest Dumbledore for sedition, he was accompanied by Kingsley Shacklebolt and which other ministry employee?

a. Bodric Bode
b. Barty Crouch Senior
c. Dawlish

8. When Dumbledore took Harry along to persuade Horace Slughorn to return as a professor to Hogwarts, he wished to take something from the muggle's home because he "loves them". What was it?

a. A knitting pattern
b. A radio
c. A TV listings guide

9. Which of the following positions has Dumbledore never held?

a. Chief Warlock of the Wizengamot
b. Professor of Transfiguration at Hogwarts School of Witchcraft and Wizardry
c. Head of the Department of International Magical Co-operation

10. What did Dumbledore tell Harry he saw when he looked into the Mirror of Erised, that Harry didin't quite believe?

a. Himself standing with his brother, Aberforth, and sister, Ariana
b. Himself holding a pair of socks
c. Himself as Minister of Magic

11. In the Life and Lies of Dumbledore, the autobiography written by Rita Skeeter, which of his acclaimed achievements was said to have mostly been discovered by someone else?

a. The Wolfsbane Potion
b. The Twelve Uses of Dragon's Blood
c. Fifty Ways to Kill a Dragon

12. The Dumbledore Family lived in Godric's Hollow, but they moved there after Percival Dumbledore (father of Albus, Aberforth and Ariana) was sent to Azkaban. Which village was their original home?

a. Budleigh Babberton
b. Ottery St. Catchpole
c. Mould-on-the-Wold

13. The Ministry of Magic passed a number of educational decrees during the campaign to discredit Dumbledore because he alleged the return of the Dark Lord. What was Educational Decree Number 22?

a. The Ministry of Magic has the right to fill a teaching vacancy with a candidate of their choice if Dumbledore failed to appoint a teacher.
b. The role of High Inquisitor at Hogwarts was created
c. All Student Organisations, Societies, Teams, Groups, and Clubs were disbanded

14. There were three plots to assassinate Dumbledore, all executed by Draco Malfoy. Which was the second plot?

a. Honey mead laced with poison intended to be given to Dumbledore as gift by Professor Slughorn
b. A bewitched necklace carried to school by Katie Bell that would kill whoever wore it
c. A tentacula plant was left under his bed to grow until it strangled him

15. At Dumbledore's funeral a mournful song was heard as his body was laid to rest. Who was singing the song?

a. Hawkes the Phoenix
b. The Hogwarts' ghosts
c. The merpeople of the Black Lake.

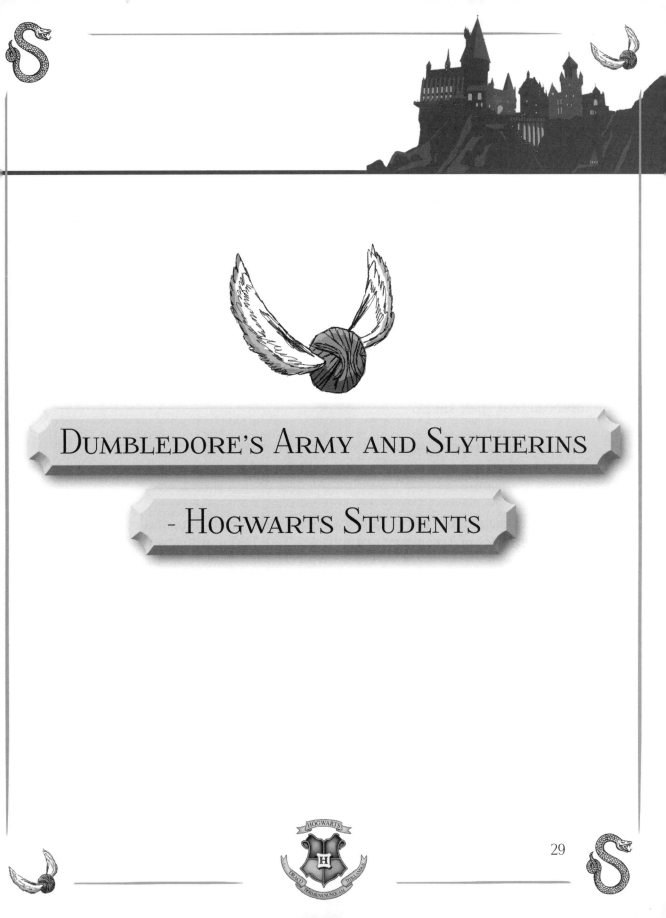

DUMBLEDORE'S ARMY AND SLYTHERINS

- HOGWARTS STUDENTS

1. In the first year at Hogwarts, thanks to last minute points awarded by Dumbledore to Harry, Ron, Hermione, and Neville (for standing up to his friends), Gryffindor won the House Cup. How many points did they win by?

a. 20

b. 15

c. 10

2. Hermione put a jinx spell on the parchment which held the names of the students in Dumbledore's Army. What was the name of Cho Chang's friend who informed Dolores Umbridge of their meetings and broke out into spots on her forehead that spelt sneak?

a. Marietta Edgecombe

b. Ernie McMillan

c. Eloise Midgeon

3. Which classmate of Harry's is just one day older than him, and could have been the subject of Trelawney's prophecy if fate had manifested differently?

a. Terry Boot

b. Neville Longbottom

c. Draco Malfoy

4. Which one of the Hufflepuff students said, "My name was down for Eton, you know; I can't tell you how glad I am I came here instead."?

a. Justin Finch-Fletchley

b. Seamus Finnegan

c. Colin Creevey

5. What is the name of the skeletal hand and arm bones that Draco carries? They were purchased in Borgin and Bourkes and is said to give light only to the carrier.

a. Torch of Light
b. Hand of Glory
c. Skeleton Flashlight

6. Fred and George Weasley gave Harry the Marauders Map to help him get to Hogsmead when Uncle Dudley wouldn't sign his permission slip. What is the correct order of the authors as shown on the map?

a. Padfoot, Prongs, Moony, and Wormtail
b. Moony, Wormtail, Padfoot, and Prongs
c. Prongs, Padfoot, Wormtail, and Moony

7. Cormac McLaggen tried out for Gryffindor Keeper in Harry's sixth year at Hogwarts. Why did Cormac miss the Quidditch try-outs in the fifth year?

a. He grew an extra leg due to a duelling accident
b. He was in detention for melting his cauldron in potions class
c. He ate a pound of doxy eggs for a bet

8. Romilda Vane had always been somewhat obsessed with Harry but in the sixth year she decided to try her luck with a love potion from Weasley's Wizard Wheezes. What was the first thing Romilda Vane offered Harry that was spiked with the love potion?

a. Gillywater
b. Cauldron Cakes
c. Fizzing Whizbees

9. Myrtle Warren was a Ravenclaw student who became Moaning Myrtle the ghost. Who teased Moaning Myrtle about her glasses, leading to her crying in the bathroom before she was killed by the Basilisk?

a. Marcella Long
b. Olive Hornby
c. Narcissus Black

10. In the First Task of the Triwizard Tournament what type of dragon did Cedric Diggory take on?

a. Hungarian Horntail
b. Swedish Short-Snout
c. Chinese Fireball
d. Common Welsh Green

11. There was a pair of twins in Hogwarts during Harry's time. One was in Gryffindor, the other in Ravenclaw. Harry and Ron took them to the Yule Ball. Which one went with Harry?

a. Pansy
b. Parvati
c. Padma

12. Neville Longbottom lives with his formidable grandmother, Augusta. What does she send him via owl post in his first year at Hogwarts?

a. A Rememberall
b. A knotted Handkerchief
c. A Howler

13. Before he realised how he felt about Ginny Weasley, Harry fancied Cho Chang, the seeker on the Ravenclaw Quidditch team. Which professional quidditch team does Cho support?

a. The Holyhead Harpies
b. The Chudley Cannons
c. The Tutshill Tornados

14. After the battle for Hogwarts, Luna distracted everyone in the Great Hall so Harry could sneak off for some peace and quiet under his invisibility cloak. What did she shout?

a. Oh look! A Blibbering Humdinger
b. I've got nargles in my head
c. Wow! Look! There's a hinkypunk

15. What did Fred and George Weasley use for their final prank before they left Hogwarts to start their joke shop?

a. Wildfire Wizzbangs
b. A portable swamp
c. Headless hats

THEY'RE QUITE GOOD AT SPELLS YOU KNOW

- HOGWARTS TEACHERS

1. As well as being Deputy Headmistress of Hogwarts, Minerva McGonagall was Professor of Transfiguration. What did she turn her desk into in Harry's first lesson?

a. A dog
b. A pig
c. A cat

2. What is the name of the teacher of Muggle Studies who was captured by the Death Eaters, killed by Lord Voldemort and fed to his snake, Nagini?

a. Clytemnestra Brown
b. Charity Burbage
c. Christina Burdock

3. Hagrid takes over as Professor for the Care of Magical Creatures after the previous teacher resigns to spend more time with his remaining limbs. Who was he?

a. Professor Grubbily-Plank
b. Professor Sinestra
c. Professor Silvanus Kettleburn

4. Who was the Headmaster of Hogwarts who was the grandfather of Sirius Black?

a. Regulus Black
b. Phineas Black
c. Priscilla Black

5. Professor Snape was called upon to substitute for one of Professor Lupin's classes during one of his "wolfish" spells. What page in the textbook did he tell the class to turn to?

a. 294
b. 432
c. 394

6. Fifth year students at Hogwarts sit their OWL exams and in year seven, sit NEWTS. We know that OWL stands for Ordinary Wizarding Level, but can you remember what NEWT stands for?

a. Nearly Everything Wizarding Test
b. Nastily Exhausting Wizarding Test
c. Normally Easy Wizarding Test

7. He lived in a house in Spinners End. He was a Death Eater who turned spy for Dumbledore. His name is Severus Snape. What were the name of his parents?

a. Toby Snape and Elly Priest
b. Tobias Snape and Ellen Prince
c. Tobias Snape and Eileen Prince

8. Gilderoy Lockhart was appointed Professor for Defence Against the Dark Arts in Harry's second year. At his first lesson he set the students a quiz – all about himself. What is the answer to the question "what is my favourite colour"?

a. Turquoise
b. Lilac
c. Aquamarine

9. What is the name of the wizard who came to Hogwarts to conduct the apparition tutorials and examined Harry?

a. Griselda Marchbanks
b. Sturgess Podmore
c. Wilkie Twycross

10. Professor Snape brewed a potion for Remus Lupin to take to prevent him turning into a werewolf on a full moon during his time as Professor for Defence Against the Dark Arts. What was the potion?

a. Wolfsbane potion
b. Essence of Dittany
c. Alihotsy Draught

11. Professor Slughorn is a gastronome. He loves fine food and wine and confectionery. What is his favourite sweet?

a. Sherbert lemons
b. Crystalized pineapple
c. Liquorice cockroaches

12. Madam Pomfrey is the matron at Hogwarts and she tended to Harry every time he was injured. After Lockhart had melted all the bones in Harry's arm what did she use that made "regrowing bones a nasty business"?

a. Skele-gro
b. Boneback
c. Calcioretrievis

13. Sybill Trelawney is the Professor of Divination at Hogwarts. Students have to climb through a trap door to reach her classroom. In which of the Hogwarts' towers is the classroom found?

a. South Tower
b. North Tower
c. East Tower

14. When Harry and Ron signed up for NEWT Potions, Harry got his hands on the Half Blood Prince's textbook. It turned out to have belonged to Severus Snape, but what was the title of the book and who was its author?

a. Advanced Potion-Making by Libatius Borage
b. Most Potente Potions by Thorfinn Rowle
c. The Practical Potioneer by Nicholas Flamel

15. In the Prisoner of Azkaban, which teacher orders a cherry syrup and soda with ice and umbrella in The Three Broomsticks?

a. Professor McGonagall
b. Albus Dumbledore
c. Professor Flitwick

The Weasleys

The Red Headed Clan

- The Weasley Family

1. The Weasley's live in a higgledy-piggledy house called The Burrow. It is not too far from the Lovegoods House, but what is the name of the nearest village?

a. Mould-on-the-Wold
b. Ottery St. Catchpole
c. Budleigh Babberton

2. What is the name of Molly Weasley's favourite singer? She sings a jazzy little number called "a cauldron full of hot, strong love".

a. Celestina Warbeck
b. Appalonya Pringle
c. Glinda Glamour

3. Charlie is the second eldest of the Weasley children. What is his job?

a. Treasure hunter for Gringotts
b. Dragon keeper in Romania
c. Ministry of Magic employee

4. Molly and Arthur Weasley have a truly loving relationship. What is Arthur's pet name for Molly he uses in private?

a. Dearest
b. Mollybabe
c. Mollywobbles

5. Which relative of the Weasley family lent Fleur Delacourt a tiara for her wedding to Bill Weasley?

a. Great Uncle Bilius
b. Great Aunt Muriel
c. Great Aunt Tessie

6. Molly Weasley is a great knitter and the kids always receive jumpers for Christmas – even Harry. Ron is never impressed because he doesn't like the colour he always receives. What colour is it?

a. Red
b. Maroon
c. Green

7. Percy was teased mercilessly by his siblings. Well he was rather pompous. Who was Percy's girlfriend at school?

a. Penelope Clearwater
b. Angelina Johnson
c. Hannah Abbott

8. George had his left ear cursed off during Harry's flight to the Burrow the day before his 17th Birthday. His twin brother Fred was killed in the Battle for Hogwarts. Whereabouts in the castle did he die?

a. In the Room of Requirement
b. In the courtyard
c. Outside the Room of Requirement

9. In the summer holiday between years two and three at school, the Weasley Family went on a trip to Egypt. How did they afford the holiday?

a. Mr. Weasley was promoted at the Ministry
b. They won the Daily Prophet Grand Galleon Prize Draw
c. From money awarded for Ron's special services to Hogwarts School.

10. After Bill and Fleur were married, they set up home together. It was used as a safe haven during the quest for the horcruxes. Where did they live?

a. The Owl House, Ottery St. Catchpole
b. Shell Cottage, Tinworth
c. Weasley Manor, Godric's Hollow

11. Ginny Weasley was a very popular girl at school and eventually married Harry, but who was her first boyfriend?

a. Dean Thomas
b. Dennis Creevey
c. Michael Corner

12. Molly Weasley does not have a regular clock that tells the time. There is a hand for every member of the family and the hands point to a different life situation such as work, travelling, home etc to identify where they are. What is at 12.00?

a. Mortal peril
b. Hospital
c. School

13. Which of Ginny Weasley's impressive spells was noticed by professor Slughorn earning her an invitation to the "Slug Club"?

a. A leg-locking jinx
b. A Bat-bogey hex
c. A reductor curse

14. Arthur Weasley loves muggles and muggle objects. He fixed Sirius' flying motorbike and made a Ford Anglia fly, but what is his greatest ambition?

a. To gain a muggle driving license
b. To learn how to use a computer
c. To learn how aeroplanes stay up

15. Who did Molly duel with and kill during the Battle of Hogwarts with a cry of "not my daughter, you bitch"?

a. Bellatrix Lestrange
b. Thorfinn Rowle
c. Fenrir Greyback

The Dark Lord

- Voldemort

1. Despite his disgust of muggles, Tom Riddle, aka, Lord Voldemort had a muggle father, Tom Riddle. Who was his witch mother?

a. Merope Gaunt
b. Marlene McKinnon
c. Gwenog Jones

2. What village did Tom Riddle and his mother call home? It was also the location to which Voldemort returned when he was planning the capture of Harry during the Triwizard Tournament?

a. Great Flashingham
b. Tiny Tittering
c. Little Hangleton

3. Dumbledore first met Tom Riddle when he was 11 years old to tell him he had a place at Hogwarts. Mrs. Cole was the gin loving head of the orphanage which had what name?

a. Wood's Orphanage
b. Wool's Orphanage
c. Wend's Orphanage

4. Tom Riddle murdered his father, grandfather, and grandmother. Who was blamed and sentenced to Azkaban prison for the crime?

a. Marvolo Gaunt
b. Morfin Gaunt
c. Martha Gaunt

5. After graduating from Hogwarts, what was Tom Riddle's first employment?

a. Professor of Defence Against the Dark Arts
b. Auror
c. A shop assistant at Borgin and Burkes

6. Voldermort was living a "half-life", barely human and barely alive when we first encounter him. Which magical creature's blood was he drinking to sustain himself?

a. Phoenix
b. Unicorn
c. Centaur

7. Voldemort collected treasures – particularly those that had belonged to the four founders of Hogwarts – to turn into horcruxes. He stole Helga Hufflepuff's silver cup from an old witch called Hepzibah Smith. Who was her house elf?

a. Dokey
b. Minky
c. Hokey

8. When Voldemort had just regained human form in the graveyard to where Harry and Cedric were transported by the Triwizard Cup portkey he cast the avada kedavra curse at Harry who responded with expelliarmus. Harry's and Voldemort's wand shared a core and the clash of spells resulted in another spell, which was?

a. Priori incantatem
b. Priori castato
c. Priori revelio

9. Who was the first Ministry of Magic employee that Voldemort used the imperius curse on in his attempt to get hold of the prophecy?

a. Sturgis Podmore
b. Bodric Bode
c. Stamford Jorkins

10. Voldemort used a "Drink of Despair" potion to protect the locket containing his horcrux. Dumbledore drank the potion to attain the locket. What colour is the potion?

a. Emerald Green
b. Dark Indigo
c. Ruby Red

11. Where did Voldemort set up Death Eater headquarters before they took over the Ministry of Magic?

a. Malfoy Manor
b. A spare room at Borgin and Burkes
c. His father's old house

12. What event caused Voldemort to realise that Harry was hunting horcruxes?

a. He tortured the information from Ollivander
b. The Gringotts' goblins informed him Bellatrix Lestrange's vault had been broken into and a cup stolen
c. He read Harry's mind using legilimency

13. At the start of the battle for control with The Order of the Phoenix and the Ministry of Magic fighting to keep Voldemort and The Death Eaters from taking over, Voldemort duelled with the Head of the Department of Magical Law Enforcement who was the aunt of one of the Hogwarts students. Who was she?

a. Helena Abbott
b. Amelia Bones
c. Cressida Clearwater

14. After the Battle for Hogwarts, Neville refuses to join Voldermort. What does the Dark Lord do to him?

a. He makes Nagini attack him
b. He makes him wear the Sorting Hat and sets it on fire
c. He tortures him with the cruciatus curse

15. Which three defenders of Hogwarts did Voldemort duel all at once in the Great Hall after it was revealed Harry had survived the killing curse?

a. Horace Slughorn, Arthur Weasley, and George Weasley
b. Kingsley Shacklebolt, Minerva McGonagall, and Molly Weasley
c. Horace Slughorn, Kingsley Shacklebolt, and Minerva McGonagall

Voldemort Loyalists

- Death Eaters

1. The Death Eaters bear the "dark mark" of Voldemort – a snake protruding from a skull. Where on the body is the mark?

a. The arm
b. The leg
c. The forehead

2. When Voldemort's wand failed to kill Harry in the graveyard, Ollivander told him to use another wand. Which Death Eater's wand did he take, which was subsequently destroyed during the flight from Privet Drive?

a. Draco Malfoy
b. Lucius Malfoy
c. Pius Thicknesse

3. Who was the leader of the gang of snatchers who captured Harry, Ron, and Hermione in a wood and took them to Malfoy Mansion?

a. Scabior
b. Stan Shunpike
c. Willie Widdershins

4. Who overheard Sybil Trelawney telling Dumbledore the prophecy and passed the information onto Lord Voldemort?

a. Peter Pettigrew
b. Fenrir Greyback
c. Severus Snape

5. What spell did Gregory Goyle cast in the Room of Requirement in the Battle for Hogwarts that he was unable to control, ultimately killing him?

a. The Expulso curse
b. Fiendfyre
c. The Disintegration curse

6. Igor Karkaroff was released from Azkaban Prison because he provided information to the Ministry of Magic about other Death Eaters. The first name he gave was Rosier, but he was already dead. Who is the ministry employee he mentioned next?

a. Albert Runcorn
b. Augustus Rookwood
c. Filius Finbok

7. What is the name of the husband of Bellatrix Lestrange?

a. Rolphius Lestrange
b. Adolphus Lestrange
c. Rodolphus Lestrange

8. People thought Peter Pettigrew had been dead for 12 years. How did he finally die?

a. He was killed during the Battle of Hogwarts
b. His own magical silver hand killed him
c. He was hit by the Killing Curse by Bellatrix Lestrange

9. Which of his faithful Death Eaters did Voldemort appoint to be the Head of Magical Law Enforcement when they had taken control of the Ministry of Magic

a. Corban Yaxley
b. Walden Macnair
c. William Rosewood

10. The note in the locket was signed R.A.B. which turned out to be the brother of Sirius Black. What did the initials stand for?

a. Raymond Archer Black
b. Regulus Arcturus Black
c. Rudolpho Arcturus Black

11. Who were the two Death Esters who found Harry, Ron, and Hermione in the Café near Tottenham Court Road after they fled from Bill and Fleur's weddings?

a. Nott and Rosier
b. Goyle and McNair
c. Rowle and Dolohov

12. Harry was wanted for questioning over the death of Dumbledore. What was the name used to describe Harry on the "wanted" posters?

a. Potty Potter
b. Undesirable Number One
c. The Boy Who Lived Who Needs to Die

13. After the death of Dumbledore, Severus Snape was appointed Headmaster of Hogwarts. Which Death Eater brother and sister also joined the staff?

a. Annetta and Amos Capron
b. Alex and Amy Carron
c. Alecto and Amycus Carrow

14. Which Death Eater declared Harry to be dead when Voldemort used the killing curse in the Dark Forest?

a. Lucius Malfoy
b. Narcissa Malfoy
c. Pius Thicknesse

15. He injured Mad-Eye Moody and Hermione in *The Order of the Phoenix*. He was present in the Astronomy Tower when Snape killed Dumbledore. He killed Remus Lupin. But who killed Antonin Dolohov in the Battle for Hogwarts?

a. Lee Jordan
b. Kingsley Shacklebolt
c. Professor Flitwick

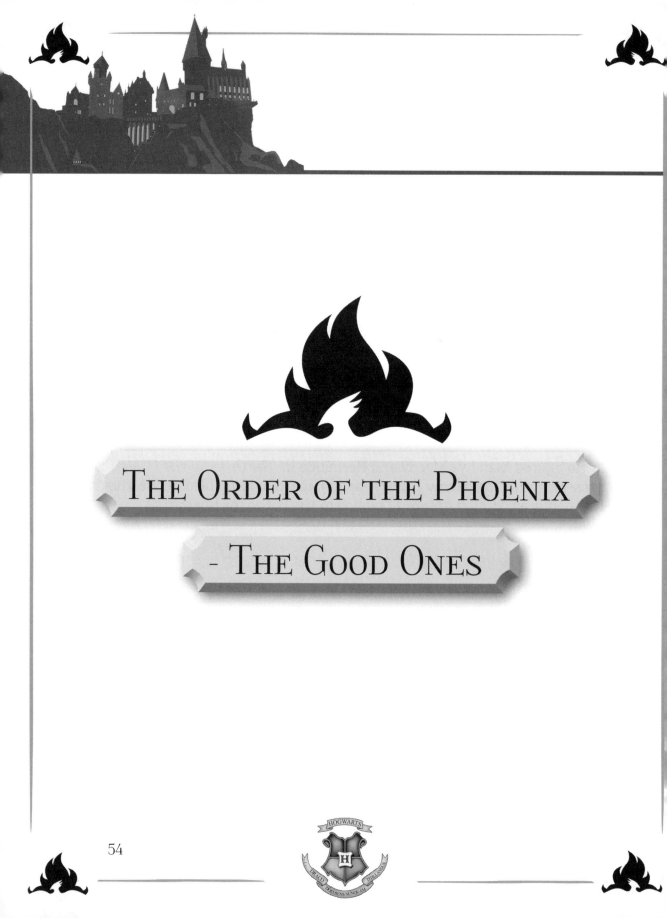

The Order of the Phoenix

- The Good Ones

1. Nymphadora Tonks who liked to be referred to as "Tonks" was a certain type of witch. She had a power to do things that amused Hermione and Ginny at 12 Grimmauld Place. What type of witch was she?

a. Animagus
b. Metamorphmagus
c. Changeling

2. A lot of the wizard families were related. How were Sirius Black and Nymphadora Tonks related?

a. Nymphadora's mother is Sirius's cousin
b. Ted Tonks is Sirius' uncle
c. They are both cousins of Molly Weasley

3. While Harry, Ron, and Hermione were away looking for Horcruxes, the Order of the Phoenix shared news via a radio program called "Potter Watch". What was Lupin's code name when he appeared on the show?

a. River
b. Romulus
c. Rapier

4. Sirius Black was locked up in Azkaban for twelve years for a crime he did not commit. How did he know that Peter Pettigrew was alive and disguised as a rat?

a. He saw a photograph in *The Daily Prophet* of Ron holding him
b. Errol the owl told him
c. Bellatrix Lestrange let it slip while she too was in the cells of Azkaban

5. Neville's parents were tortured into madness by the cruciatus spell, one of the unforgiveable spells, by Bellatrix Lestrange and Barty Crouch Junior among others. They live permanently in St. Mungo's Hospital for Magical Maladies and Injuries. Which ward are they in?

a. Dilys Derwent Ward
b. Janus Thickey Ward
c. Augustus Pye Ward

6. When Harry went to the Forbidden Forest to face his death at the hands of Lord Voldemort he conjured up some past members of The Order of the Phoenix using the Resurrection Stone. Name them.

a. Lily Potter, James Potter, Sirius Black, and Remus Lupin
b. Lily Potter, James Potter, Remus Lupin, and Nymphadora Tonks
c. James Potter, Remus Lupin, Peter Pettigrew, and Sirius Black

7. Kinglsey Shacklebolt sent his patronus to warn everyone at Bill and Fleur's wedding that the Ministry of Magic had fallen to the Death Eaters. What form does his patronus take?

a. Unicorn
b. Lynx
c. Wolf

8. Why did Hagrid have to leave Hogwarts while Harry and gang were searching for horcruxes and Snape was headmaster?

a. He hosted a "Support Harry Potter Party" in his cabin
b. He started handing out "Support Harry Potter" badges in class
c. He started cheering for Harry Potter in the Great Hall

9. When the Weasleys and Harry moved into 12 Grimmauld Place, Molly set them to work cleaning. Which of the following household spell books did she refer to for getting rid of doxies?

a. Eggs-pelliarmus. 1001 Spells for Banishing Magical stains
b. Gilderoy Lockhart's Guide to Household Pests
c. Many Ways to Charm Magical Pests From Your Home

10. In the photograph of the original Order of the Phoenix, who was pointed out to Harry because she had been killed."

a. Dorcas Meadows
b. Emmeline Vance
c. Marlene McKinnon

11. Which member of the Order was part of the advance guard who escorted the Dursleys to safety and had a large pocket watch that shouted, "hurry up"?

a. Caradoc Dearborn
b. Dedalus Diggle
c. Elphias Doge

Muggles

- Non-Magic Folk

1. Vernon Dudley works for a drill company. What was the company's name?

a. Mason and Company
b. Grunnings
c. Wilkins and Co.

2. Arabella Figg is not a muggle but not a witch either. She is what is known as a squib. What was in the bag that she hit Mundungus Fletcher with when he abandoned his post keeping watch on Harry?

a. 5-day old fruit cake
b. A new pair of slippers
c. Tins of cat food

3. Dudley is the pampered, spoilt son of Petunia and Vernon Dursley. They call him all sorts of sickening nicknames. Which of these is not one of them?

a. Big D
b. Popkin
c. Pudding-pie
d. Diddykins
e. Dudders

4. The Dursleys and Harry went to the zoo for Dudley's birthday where Harry accidently freed a snake. Who was Dudley's friend who went on the trip with them?

a. Piers Polkiss
b. Dennis Dilby
c. Greg Grindle

5. When Uncle Vernon's sister, Aunt Marge, came to stay, which school did Vernon say he sent Harry to?

a. St. Gregory's
b. St. Brutus' Secure Centre for Incurably Criminal Boys
c. Woolworth Academy

6. When Aunt Marge upset Harry by denigrating his parents she blew up into a giant balloon.'. Where did the Minister of Magic say she was found?

a. Sheffield
b. Southampton
c. Sunderland

7. At Uncle Vernon's dinner party, Harry spoilt his Japanese golfer joke and Dobby spoiled Aunt Petunia's pudding. Who were the guests of honour?

a. Mr. Macmillan, Dudley's headmaster, and his wife
b. Mr Mason, a builder and his wife
c. Mr Smith, a hardware magnate, and his wife

8. The Order of the Phoenix agreed to get the Dursleys to a place of safety when the enchantments keeping Harry safe at Number 4 Privet Drive broke on his 17th birthday. Harry watched Uncle Vernon packing and unpacking and repacking and found some hilarity in one incident. Which was?

a. When he collided with a tree and collapsed with much swearing
b. When the car boot door shut on him
c. When Dudley had added his dumb bells to a bag and he had collapsed with roars of pain and much swearing

9. Why were the Dursley's so embarrassed and disgusted to receive a letter from Molly Weasley?

a. It was delivered by Errol, the clumsy owl
b. It was covered in stamps
c. It bellowed loudly when opened

10. Which of these have the Dursleys never given Harry as a birthday or Christmas present?

a. A fifty-pence piece
b. A toothpick
c. A rubber band
d. A wire coat hanger

Magical Creatures

- Fantastic Beasts, Goblins, Elves and Ghosts

1. Hogwarts is home to several ghosts, with each house having their own special spirit. What is the nickname of Rowena Ravenclaw, the ghost of Ravenclaw Tower?

a. The Iron Lady
b. The Grey Lady
c. The Green Lady

2. The Beauxbatons Students arrived at Hogwarts in a coach pulled by a dozen winged horses. The horses had a special diet, which includes which drink?

a. Gillywater
b. Butterbeer
c. Single Malt Whisky

3. The Forbidden Forest is home to a number of magical creatures including a herd of centaurs, most of whom became increasingly hostile to humans throughout the series. Who is their leader?

a. Bane
b. Magorian
c. Ronan

4. Hagrid had always wanted a pet dragon and he finally got an egg which hatched into a dragon he named Norbert (later changed to Norberta when it was found it was a she dragon). What breed of dragon was it?

a. Yellow Reaper
b. Common English Brown
c. Norwegian Ridgeback

5. During the second task in the Triwizard Tournament, Fleur was prevented from rescuing her sister by some magical creatures who live in the Black Lake. Which creatures?

a. Merpeople
b. Grindylow
c. Niffler

6. Fleur Delacour is a special type of witch. These witches are beautiful women with white-gold hair and skin that appears to shine moon-bright. They have the power to bewitch men but are not so nice when they are angry as their faces elongate into sharp, cruel-beaked bird heads, and long scaly wings burst from their shoulders. What is this type of witch called?

a. Vespa
b. Veela
c. Velma

7. There are hippogriffs in the Forbidden Forest. To avoid them attacking you, how do you greet a hippogriff?

a. Stroke its beak
b. Bow to it
c. Offer it food

8. Hagrid has some funny ideas of cute creatures and what makes a good pet. He bred a weird creature called a blast-ended skrewt . Which two animals did he cross breed to achieve this?

a. A fire crab and a manticore
b. Fire salamander and a manticore
c. A dragon and flobberworm

9. After Dobby left the Malfoy Family and struggled to find a job because he wanted payment for his work, Dumbledore employed him in the kitchens of Hogwarts. What was his weekly wage?

a. 10 galleons
b. 5 galleons
c. 1 galleon

10. Xenophilius Lovegood was convinced the ornament he had in his home was a horn from a crumple-horned snorkack. What was it really?

a. An erumpent horn
b. A nargle
c. A troll's weapon

11. Every magic wand is made of wood but has a core of something special from a magical creature. Which of the following substances is not known to be used in wand cores?

a. Phoenix feather
b. Unicorn hair
c. Hippogriff feather

12. Aragog is an acromantula raised by Hagrid in Hogwarts Castle who then moved into the Forbidden Forest, where he took a wife and raised a huge family. What was his wife's name?

a. Morag
b. Mosag
c. Aramag

13. In the maze in the Triwizard Tournament, Harry met Sphinx who set him a riddle he must solve in order to get past. What was the answer to the riddle?

a. Spider
b. Spy
c. Traitor

14. How do you find a knarl among a group of hedgehogs?

a. Bow to each one and see which one bows back
b. Offer each one some milk
c. See which one will lead you to gold.

15. In their second year, the students were asked to repot mandrakes in one of Professor Sprout's herbology lessons. Mandrake root can unpetrify creatures turned to stone but what is the dangerous magical power of a mandrake?

a. Touching the leaves causes a rash of boils
b. Its cry is fatal to anyone who hears it
c. It has a venomous bite

WELCOME TO

HOGSMEADE

THE ONLY ALL-WIZARDING VILLAGE IN BRITAIN

- HOGSMEADE

1. What is the name of the barmaid of the Three Broomsticks of whom Hermione says, "Ron fancies her"?

a. Madame Rosmerta
b. Madame Esberta
c. Madame Rosanna

2. Where do Harry and Cho go in Hogsmeade on their unsuccessful Valentine's Day date?

a. The Hogs Head
b. Madame Puddifoot's Tea Shop
c. Honeydukes Sweet Shop

3. What is the name of the Wizarding joke store in Hogsmeade that Fred and George visited often?

a. Zonko's Joke Shop
b. Dervish and Bangs
c. Bozo's Gags and Games

4. When Harry, Ron, and Hermione went to Hogsmeade after fleeing from Gringotts Bank, they set off a charm set by the Death Eaters to warn of their arrival. What was the charm?

a. Screeching charm
b. Caterwauling charm
c. Howling charm

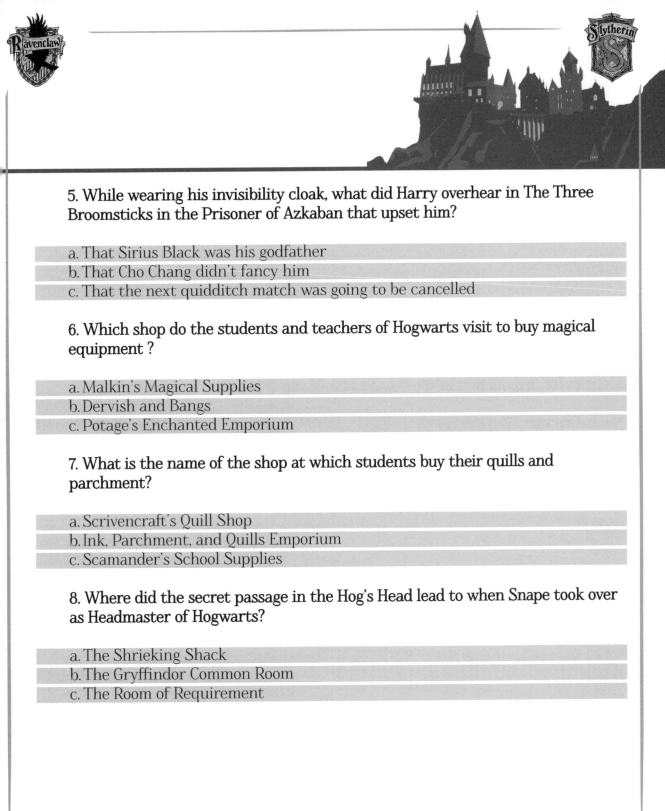

5. While wearing his invisibility cloak, what did Harry overhear in The Three Broomsticks in the Prisoner of Azkaban that upset him?

a. That Sirius Black was his godfather
b. That Cho Chang didn't fancy him
c. That the next quidditch match was going to be cancelled

6. Which shop do the students and teachers of Hogwarts visit to buy magical equipment ?

a. Malkin's Magical Supplies
b. Dervish and Bangs
c. Potage's Enchanted Emporium

7. What is the name of the shop at which students buy their quills and parchment?

a. Scrivencraft's Quill Shop
b. Ink, Parchment, and Quills Emporium
c. Scamander's School Supplies

8. Where did the secret passage in the Hog's Head lead to when Snape took over as Headmaster of Hogwarts?

a. The Shrieking Shack
b. The Gryffindor Common Room
c. The Room of Requirement

9. How many bottles of butterbeer did Fred and George order at the bar of the Hog's Head when a group of students, who were later to become Dumbledore's Army, gathered to hear Hermione's idea?

a. 15
b. 20
c. 25

10. From which clothes shop that sells all sorts of quirky items for the fashionable witch and wizard does Harry buy Dobby a selection of socks to thank him for helping him in the second task of the Triwizard Tournament?

a. Gladrags Wizardwear
b. Witchy Fashions
c. Gilderoy's Style and Fashion

DIAGON ALLEY

- THE LEAKY CAULDRON, GRINGOTTS AND THE SHOPS

1. When Harry first entered the Leaky Cauldron, he was recognised by Tom who exclaimed and announced his arrival to the pub. Who was the person who kept coming up to shake Harry's hand?

a. Dedalus Diggle
b. Doris Crockford
c. Professor Quirrell

2. What is the sequence of bricks to open the archway in the wall to enter Diagon Alley?

a. Three up and two down from the trash can
b. Three across and two up from the trash can
c. Four up and three across

3. Most witches and wizards in the UK buy their wands at Ollivander's. Which year was Ollivander's founded?

a. 57 BC
b. 465 BC
c. 382 BC

4. On his first visit to Diagon Alley, a group of people were admiring a Nimbus 2000 in a shop window. Which shop was it?

a. Quality Quidditch Supplies
b. Quirrell's Quidditch Supplies
c. Brooms for All Occasions

5. There is a warning inscribed above the door of Gringotts Bank. The first two lines are "Enter, stranger, but take heed of what awaits the sin of greed". What are the next two lines?

a. For those who take, but do not earn, must pay most dearly in their turn
b. So if you seek beneath our floors, a treasure that was never yours
c. Thief, you have been warned, beware, of finding more than treasure there

6. What specific cauldron do first years have to buy from Potage's Cauldron Shop?

a. Size 3 lead cauldron
b. Size 2 pewter cauldron
c. Size 1 tin cauldron

7. The first time Harry took the Knight Bus, his destination was the Leaky Cauldron. The fare is either ticket only, or ticket and a hot chocolate. How much does the latter fare cost?

a. 12 sickles
b. 13 sickles
c. 14 sickles

8. There are two shops selling wizard robes in Diagon Alley. Madam Malkin's is one. Which is the other?

a. Twilfit and Tattings
b. Gambol and Japes
c. Debenhams Outfitters

9. What is the name of the shop that sells owls, from which Hagrid purchased Hedwig for Harry?

a. Eeylops Owl Emporium
b. The Owlery
c. Ephraim's Owl Emporium

10. What is the number of the vault from which Hagrid removed the Philosopher's Stone to take for safekeeping at Hogwarts?

a. 317
b. 137
c. 713

11. Which game did Harry resist buying in Diagon Alley while he was staying at the Leaky Cauldron?

a. A sold gold wizarding chess set
b. A solid gold gobstones set
c. A solid mahogany wizarding chess set

12. In *The Prisoner of Azkaban*, Harry stayed at the Leaky Cauldron before school starts. Which Diagon Alley shopkeeper helped Harry with his History of Magic Homework?

a. Florian Fortescue
b. Madam Malkin
c. Tom, the barkeeper

13. What is the name of the disreputable street just off Diagon Alley where Harry ends up after using Floo Powder at The Burrow?

a. Leadenhall Market
b. Knockturn Alley
c. Dragon Street

14. At which shop would you buy Dr. Filibuster's Fabulous, Wet-Start, No-Heat Fireworks

a. Weasley's Wizard Wheezes
b. Slug and Jiggers Apothecary
c. Gambol and Japes

15. He is a large ginger cat with a squashed flat face and bottle-brush tail. Where did Hermione purchase Crookshanks?

a. Magical Menagerie
b. All Creatures Great and Small
c. Kettleburn's Creature Shop

Ministry of Magic

- Staff and Rooms

1. Arthur Weasley worked in the Office for the Misuse of Muggle Artefacts at the Ministry of Magic. He shared his pokey little office which had no windows with who?

a. Purefoy
b. Perkins
c. Popkiss

2. When Arthur Weasley took Harry to the Ministry of Magic they used the public entrance which was a red telephone box. Which numbers needed to be dialled to gain entry?

a. 62442
b. 42664
c. 66666

3. She sent Harry his "you are expelled from Hogwarts" letter and was later impersonated by Hermione using Polyjuice potion when Hermione, Harry and Ron went to the ministry to get the locket from Umbridge. Name the witch.

a. Melina Creen
b. Mafalda Hopkirk
c. Adalbert Waffling

4. Who was the Minister for Magic who delivered Dumbledore's will to Harry, Ron, and Hermione on the day of Bill and Fleur's wedding?

a. Cornelius Fudge
b. Rufus Scrimgeour
c. Kingsley Shacklebolt

5. When the Death Eaters took over the Ministry, Yaxley was appointed as Head of Magical Law Enforcement. He cornered Ron (Reg Cattermole) in the lift to complain his office was still raining. What spell did Arthur Weasley suggest Ron try?

a. Precipitato finite
b. Umbrellicus
c. Meteolojinx recant

6. What was the name of the Ministry of Magic employee who went missing on her holiday to Albania, who it turned out had been killed by Lord Voldemort?

a. Bertha Jorkins
b. Amelia Bones
c. Hestia Jones

7. Buckbeak the Hippogriff was sentenced to death by the Ministry. What is the full name of the department that deals with the magic animal kingdom?

a. Beasts, Beings, and Spirit Division
b. Department for the Regulation and Control of Magical Creatures
c. Pest Advisory Bureau

8. Harry's trial for underage magic was conducted in the courtrooms of the Ministry of Magic which were on the same level as the Department of Mysteries, which we visited again in The Order of the Phoenix. What level is the Department of Mysteries on?

a. Level seven
b. Level eight
c. Level nine

9. Voldemort wanted to hear the prophecy made about Harry. It was kept in the Hall of Prophecy in the Ministry of Magic. There were rows and rows of glass orbs. Which row contained Harry's prophecy?

a. 97
b. 77
c. 57

10. A Ministry of Magic employee - an Unspeakable in the Department of Mysteries - was strangled by a tentacula plant in St. Mungo's Hospital for Magical Maladies and Injuries to prevent him telling tales after the effects on an Imperius curse wore off. Who was he?

a. Albert Runcorn
b. Broderick Bode
c. Dirk Cresswell

11. After leaving her position as Professor of Defence Against the Dark Arts at Hogwarts, Dolores Umbridge became Head of The Muggle Born Registration Committee. She acquired the locket containing Voldemort's horcrux. Who did she say the initial S referred to? She was related to the family.

a. The Selwyn Family
b. The Scrivenshaft Family
c. The Sugden Family

12. In the foyer of the Ministry of Magic there is a large water feature called the Fountain of Magical Brethren. What are the creatures that make up the fountain's statue?

a. Wizard, witch, centaur, goblin, and owl
b. Wizard, witch, centaur, house-elf, and goblin
c. Wizard, witch, centaur, goblin, and muggle

13. What is the name of the Ministry department that is responsible for modifying the memories of Muggles who have been exposed to magic?

a. Unspeakables
b. Obliviators
c. Aurors

14. In his sixth year Ron was advised to "sever all ties" with Harry Potter. Who delivered this advice?

a. Percy Weasley
b. Cornelius Fudge
c. Severus Snape

15. Fred and George bet all their savings on the final of the Quidditch World Cup. Who paid them in Leprechaun gold (which disappears) and then refused to pay them properly?

a. Seamus Finnegan
b. Ludo Bagman
c. Barty Crouch Senior

THE WIDER

WIZARDING WORLD

1. In the UK, wizard and witch criminals are locked up in Azkaban Prison. In which prison was Gellert Grindlewald confined?

a. Nuremburg
b. Nurmengard
c. Northanger

2. At Bill and Fleur's wedding we met Fleur's parents, but her father was only ever referred to as Monsieur Delacour. What is Fleur's mother's name?

a. Apolline
b. Angelique
c. Arabella

3. British wizards and witches get their wands from Ollivander's. Who is the celebrated European wand maker who is known to have possessed the elder wand before Grindlewald stole it?

a. Raonic
b. Gregorovitch
c. Randiantic

4. One of the passengers on Harry's first trip on the Knight Bus was Madame Marsh. What was her destination?

a. Godric's Hollow
b. Moreton-in-Marsh
c. Abergavenny

5. Rita Skeeter is a journalist for the Daily Prophet with a propensity for exaggeration and over-dramatisation. Which type of quill does she use most often?

a. Smart-answer quill
b. Quick quotes quill
c. Scrivenshaft's phoenix feather

6. How many broomsticks are flown in a full game of Quidditch?

a. 13
b. 15
c. 17

7. What is the spell that notifies a wizard that there are other humans in a dwelling?

a. Homenum finista
b. Homosefia
c. Homenum revelio

8. To master the apparition spell, there are three "D"s. Which is the first of them, according to Wilkie Twycross?

a. Determination
b. Destination
c. Deliberation

9. What is the name of the move in Quidditch where the seeker fakes seeing the snitch and dives to the ground but pulls out of the dive just in time, but the opposing seeker plummets to the ground?

a. Wonky Fent
b. Wonky Faint
c. Wronski Feint

10. Which magical object causes people to turn orange and sprout wart-like tentacles?

a. Metamorph medals
b. Decoy detonators
c. U-No-Poo

11. What is the spell to create the Dark Mark?

a. Serpentsentia
b. Morsmorde
c. Summonatus

12. Which of Ginny's books did Lucius Malfoy slip Tom Riddle's diary into when everyone was in Flourish and Blotts?

a. The Standard Book of Spells Grade 2 by Miranda Goshawk
b. A History of Magic by Bathilda Bagshott
c. A Beginner's Guide to Transfiguration by Emeric Switch

13. In the epilogue we learn that Draco Malfoy has married. What is his son's name?

a. Lucian
b. Tom
c. Scorpius

14. Why did Alastor Moody warn Harry not to put his wand in his back pocket?

a. Because it would break and leave a splinter in his bum
b. It would ignite and burn his buttocks
c. It would get stuck

15. What did Grawp call Hermione because he can't say her full name?

a. Hermy
b. Mione
c. Moaney

16. Why did classroom 11 at Hogwarts have to be turned into a forest-like space?

a. The Whomping Willow's roots had sprung through the floor
b. One of Fred and George's pranks went wrong
c. Firenze took over Divination lessons and centaurs can't climb stairs

17. When Buckbeak the Hippogriff went on the run with Sirius Black he was given a new name. What was it?'

a. Beaky
b. Featherwings
c. Witherwings

18. Let's talk wizarding money. How many knuts are in a sickle and how many sickles are there in a galleon?

a. 29 knuts in a sickle, 17 sickles in a galleon
b. 27 knuts in a sickle, 15 sickles in a galleon
c. 23 knuts in a sickle, 13 sickles in a galleon

19. What language do goblins speak?

a. Goblinish
b. Gobbledegook
c. Gibberish

20. What is the name of the Wizard Court of the Ministry of Magic?

a. Wizencourt
b. Wizengamot
c. Mugwump Council

CHILDREN'S

SECTION

1. What number Privet Drive do the Dursleys live?

a. 4
b. 14
c. 44

2. Harry was born on July 31st 1980. What is his middle name?

a. Jeremy
b. James
c. Justin

3. Ron Weasley is Harry's best friend. How many brothers does Ron have?

a. Five
b. Four
c. Three

4. What form does Luna Lovegood's patronus take?

a. Otter
b. Spaniel
c. Rabbit

5. What form does Rita Skeeter, the daily prophet reporter, take as an animagus?

a. Snake
b. Beetle
c. Bird

6. What did Harry carve onto the rock marking Dobby's grave?

a. Here lies an elf I freed
b. Dobby was a great elf
c. Here lies Dobby, a free elf

7. What was the name of the dog Aunt Marge brought with her when she came to stay with the Dursleys?

a. Ruby
b. Ripper
c. Grubber

8. Who is the mischievous ghost who lives at Hogwarts?

a. Peeves
b. Burke
c. Diggle

9. What is the name of the clumsy Weasley family owl?

a. Eric
b. Errol
c. Ernie

10. What is the full name of the Gryffindor ghost, Nearly-Headless Nick?

a. Nicholas Flamel
b. Nicholas
c. Sir Nicholas de Mimsy-Porpington

11. Who wrote the History of Magic textbook used at Hogwarts?

a. Adalbert Waffling
b. Bathilda Bagshot
c. Arsenius Jiggle

12. What is the name of the cat belonging to Hogwarts caretaker, Argus Filch?

a. Mrs. Norris
b. Mr. Tibbles
c. Mrs. Figg

13. Which creatures feed on people's happy emotions?

a. Boggarts
b. Dementors
c. Grindylows

14. Which of Ron's brothers was a prefect in Ron's first year?

a. Fred
b. George
c. Percy

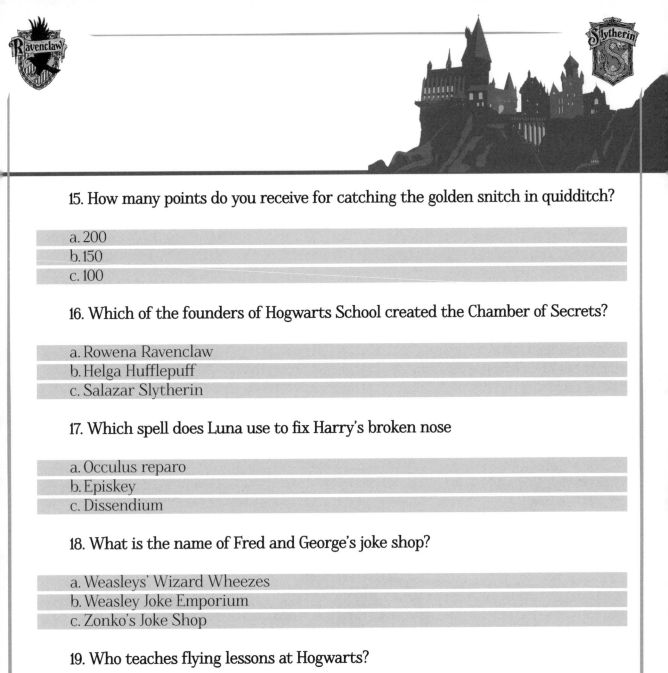

15. How many points do you receive for catching the golden snitch in quidditch?

a. 200
b. 150
c. 100

16. Which of the founders of Hogwarts School created the Chamber of Secrets?

a. Rowena Ravenclaw
b. Helga Hufflepuff
c. Salazar Slytherin

17. Which spell does Luna use to fix Harry's broken nose

a. Occulus reparo
b. Episkey
c. Dissendium

18. What is the name of Fred and George's joke shop?

a. Weasleys' Wizard Wheezes
b. Weasley Joke Emporium
c. Zonko's Joke Shop

19. Who teaches flying lessons at Hogwarts?

a. Madame Hooch
b. Charity Burbage
c. Professor Grubbly-Plank

20. Which of these spells is not one of the three unforgiveable curses?

a. The Cruciatus Curse
b. Sectumsempra
c. The Imperius Curse

21. Which of these is not a member of The Order of The Phoenix?

a. Remus Lupin
b. Mad-Eye Moody
c. Cornelius Fudge

22. What is a witch or wizard who can't do magic known as?

a. Squib
b. Muggle
c. Wiznot

23. What is the command to close the Marauders' Map?

a. All done
b. Mischief managed
c. I solemnly swear I am up to no good

24. What three balls are used in quidditch?

a. Wizzers, floosies, and snitches
b. Bludgers, quellers, and snitches
c. Quaffles, bludgers, and snitches

25. Who is the conductor of the Knight Bus?

a. Ernie Prang
b. Stan Shunpike
c. Dennis Javelin

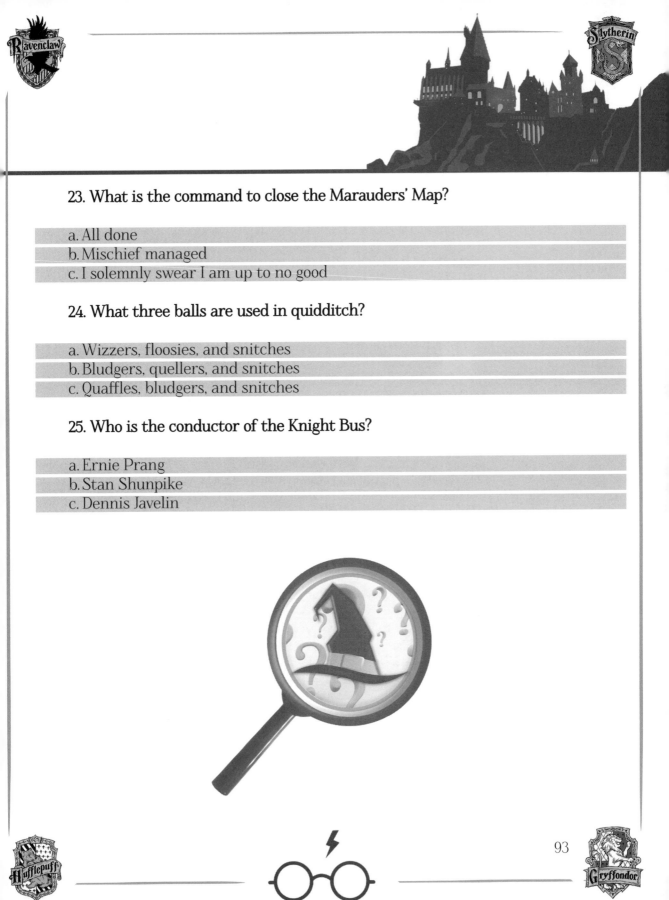

Answers

Hogwarts - A History
P:5-Q:1-Ans:A | P:5-Q:2-Ans:C | P:5-Q:3-Ans: B | P:5-Q:4-Ans: B
P:6-Q:5-Ans:A | P:6-Q:6-Ans:B | P:6-Q:7-Ans: C | P:6-Q:8-Ans: B
P:7-Q:9-Ans:C | P:7-Q:10-Ans:C | P:7-Q:11-Ans: C | P:7-Q:12-Ans: A
P:8-Q:13-Ans:B | P:8-Q:14-Ans:C | P:8-Q:15-Ans: B

The Boy Who Lived – Harry
P:10-Q:1-Ans:B | P:10-Q:2-Ans:A | P:10-Q:3-Ans: B | P:10-Q:4-Ans: B
P:11-Q:5-Ans:A | P:11-Q:6-Ans:C | P:11-Q:7-Ans: B | P:11-Q:8-Ans: B
P:12-Q:9-Ans:B | P:12-Q:10-Ans:C | P:12-Q:11-Ans: A | P:12-Q:12-Ans: C
P:13-Q:13-Ans:B | P:13-Q:14-Ans:A | P:13-Q:15-Ans: C

The Brightest Witch of Her Age – Hermione
P:15-Q:1-Ans:B | P:15-Q:2-Ans:B | P:15-Q:3-Ans: C | P:15-Q:4-Ans: A
P:16-Q:5-Ans:B | P:16-Q:6-Ans:B | P:16-Q:7-Ans: C | P:16-Q:8-Ans: B
P:17-Q:9-Ans:A | P:17-Q:10-Ans:B | P:17-Q:11-Ans: B | P:17-Q:12-Ans: C
P:18-Q:13-Ans:B | P:18-Q:14-Ans:A | P:18-Q:15-Ans: B

Harry's Best Friend – Ron
P:20-Q:1-Ans:B | P:20-Q:2-Ans:A | P:20-Q:3-Ans: A | P:20-Q:4-Ans: A
P:21-Q:5-Ans:B | P:21-Q:6-Ans:C | P:21-Q:7-Ans: B | P:21-Q:8-Ans: A
P:22-Q:9-Ans:C | P:22-Q:10-Ans:B | P:22-Q:11-Ans: A | P:22-Q:12-Ans: C
P:23-Q:13-Ans:B | P:23-Q:14-Ans:A | P:23-Q:15-Ans: C

Albus Dumbledore -The Greatest Wizard Ever
P:25-Q:1-Ans:A | P:25-Q:2-Ans:B | P:25-Q:3-Ans: C | P:25-Q:4-Ans: B
P:26-Q:5-Ans:C | P:26-Q:6-Ans:A | P:26-Q:7-Ans: C | P:26-Q:8-Ans: A
P:27-Q:9-Ans:C | P:27-Q:10-Ans:B | P:27-Q:11-Ans: B | P:27-Q:12-Ans: C
P:28-Q:13-Ans:A | P:28-Q:14-Ans:A | P:28-Q:15-Ans: C

Dumbledore's Army and Slytherins – Hogwarts students .
P:30-Q:1-Ans:C | P:30-Q:2-Ans:A | P:30-Q:3-Ans: B | P:30-Q:4-Ans: A
P:31-Q:5-Ans:B | P:31-Q:6-Ans:B | P:31-Q:7-Ans: C | P:31-Q:8-Ans: A
P:32-Q:9-Ans:B | P:32-Q:10-Ans:B | P:32-Q:11-Ans: B | P:32-Q:12-Ans: A
P:33-Q:13-Ans:C | P:33-Q:14-Ans:A | P:33-Q:15-Ans: B

They're Quite Good at Spells You Know – Hogwarts teachers
P:35-Q:1-Ans:B | P:35-Q:2-Ans:B | P:35-Q:3-Ans: C | P:35-Q:4-Ans: B
P:36-Q:5-Ans:C | P:36-Q:6-Ans:B | P:36-Q:7-Ans: C | P:36-Q:8-Ans: B
P:37-Q:9-Ans:C | P:37-Q:10-Ans:A | P:37-Q:11-Ans: B | P:37-Q:12-Ans: A
P:38-Q:13-Ans:B | P:38-Q:14-Ans:A | P:38-Q:15-Ans: C

The Red Headed Clan – the Weasley Family .
P:40-Q:1-Ans:B | P:40-Q:2-Ans:A | P:40-Q:3-Ans:B | P:40-Q:4-Ans:C
P:41-Q:5-Ans:B | P:41-Q:6-Ans:B | P:41-Q:7-Ans:A | P:41-Q:8-Ans:C
P:42-Q:9-Ans:B | P:42-Q:10-Ans:B | P:42-Q:11-Ans:C | P:42-Q:12-Ans:A
P:43-Q:13-Ans:B | P:43-Q:14-Ans:C | P:43-Q:15-Ans:A

The Dark Lord – Voldemort

P:45-Q:1-Ans:A | P:45-Q:2-Ans:C | P:45-Q:3-Ans:B | P:45-Q:4-Ans:B
P:46-Q:5-Ans:C | P:46-Q:6-Ans:B | P:46-Q:7-Ans:C | P:46-Q:8-Ans:A
P:47-Q:9-Ans:A | P:47-Q:10-Ans:A | P:47-Q:11-Ans:A | P:47-Q:12-Ans:B
P:48-Q:13-Ans:B | P:48-Q:14-Ans:B | P:48-Q:15-Ans:C

Voldemort Loyalists – Death Eaters

P:50-Q:1-Ans:A | P:50-Q:2-Ans:B | P:50-Q:3-Ans:A | P:50-Q:4-Ans:C
P:51-Q:5-Ans:B | P:51-Q:6-Ans:B | P:51-Q:7-Ans:C | P:51-Q:8-Ans:B
P:52-Q:9-Ans:A | P:52-Q:10-Ans:B | P:52-Q:11-Ans:C | P:52-Q:12-Ans:B
P:53-Q:13-Ans:C | P:53-Q:14-Ans:B | P:53-Q:15-Ans:C

The Order of the Phoenix – The Good Ones

P:55-Q:1-Ans:Bb | P:55-Q:2-Ans:A | P:55-Q:3-Ans:B | P:55-Q:4-Ans:A
P:56-Q:5-Ans:B | P:56-Q:6-Ans:A | P:56-Q:7-Ans:B | P:56-Q:8-Ans:A
P:57-Q:9-Ans:B | P:57-Q:10-Ans:C | P:57-Q:11-Ans:B

Muggles – Non-Magic Folk

P:59-Q:1-Ans:B | P:59-Q:2-Ans:C | P:59-Q:3-Ans:C | P:59-Q:4-Ans:A
P:60-Q:5-Ans:B | P:60-Q:6-Ans:A | P:60-Q:7-Ans:B | P:60-Q:8-Ans:C
P:61-Q:9-Ans:B | P:61-Q:10-Ans:C

Magical Creatures - fantastic beasts, goblins, elves, and ghosts

P:63-Q:1-Ans:B | P:63-Q:2-Ans:C | P:63-Q:3-Ans:B | P:63-Q:4-Ans:C
P:64-Q:5-Ans:B | P:64-Q:6-Ans:B | P:64-Q:7-Ans:B | P:64-Q:8-Ans:A
P:65-Q:9-Ans:C | P:65-Q:10-Ans:A | P:65-Q:11-Ans:C | P:65-Q:12-Ans:B
P:66-Q:13-Ans:A | P:66-Q:14-Ans:B | P:66-Q:15-Ans:B

The Only All-Wizarding Village in Britain – Hogsmeade

P:68-Q:1-Ans:A | P:68-Q:2-Ans:B | P:68-Q:3-Ans:A | P:68-Q:4-Ans:B
P:69-Q:5-Ans:A | P:69-Q:6-Ans:B | P:69-Q:7-Ans:A | P:69-Q:8-Ans:C
P:70-Q:9-Ans:C | P:70-Q:10-Ans:A

Diagon Alley – the Leaky Cauldron, Gringotts, and the shops

P:72-Q:1-Ans:B | P:72-Q:2-Ans:A | P:72-Q:3-Ans:C | P:72-Q:4-Ans:A
P:73-Q:5-Ans:A | P:73-Q:6-Ans:B | P:73-Q:7-Ans:C | P:73-Q:8-Ans:A
P:74-Q:9-Ans:A | P:74-Q:10-Ans:C | P:74-Q:11-Ans:B | P:74-Q:12-Ans:A
P:75-Q:13-Ans:B | P:75-Q:14-Ans:C | P:75-Q:15-Ans:A

Ministry of Magic – staff and rooms

P:77-Q:1-Ans:B | P:77-Q:2-Ans:A | P:77-Q:3-Ans:B | P:77-Q:4-Ans:B
P:78-Q:5-Ans:C | P:78-Q:6-Ans:A | P:78-Q:7-Ans:B | P:78-Q:8-Ans:C
P:79-Q:9-Ans:A | P:79-Q:10-Ans:B | P:79-Q:11-Ans:A | P:79-Q:12-Ans:B
P:80-Q:13-Ans:B | P:80-Q:14-Ans:A | P:80-Q:15-Ans:B

The Wider Wizarding World

P:82-Q:1-Ans:B | P:82-Q:2-Ans:A | P:82-Q:3-Ans:B | P:82-Q:4-Ans:C
P:83-Q:5-Ans:B | P:83-Q:6-Ans:B | P:83-Q:7-Ans:C | P:83-Q:8-Ans:B
P:84-Q:9-Ans:C | P:84-Q:10-Ans:A | P:84-Q:11-Ans:B | P:84-Q:12-Ans:C
P:85-Q:13-Ans:C | P:85-Q:14-Ans:B | P:85-Q:15-Ans:A | P:85-Q:16-Ans:C
P:86-Q:17-Ans:C | P:86-Q:18-Ans:A | P:86-Q:19-Ans:B | P:86-Q:20-Ans:B

Children's section

P:88-Q:1-Ans:A | P:88-Q:2-Ans:B | P:88-Q:3-Ans:A | P:88-Q:4-Ans:C | P:88-Q:5-Ans:B
P:89-Q:6-Ans:C | P:89-Q:7-Ans:B | P:89-Q:8-Ans:A | P:89-Q:9-Ans:B
P:90-Q:10-Ans:C | P:90-Q:11-Ans:B | P:90-Q:12-Ans:A | P:90-Q:13-Ans:B | P:90-Q:14-Ans:C
P:91-Q:15-Ans:B | P:91-Q:16-Ans:C | P:91-Q:17-Ans:B | P:91-Q:18-Ans:A | P:91-Q:19-Ans:A
P:92-Q:20-Ans:B | P:92-Q:21-Ans:C | P:92-Q:22-Ans:A
P:93-Q:23-Ans:B | P:93-Q:24-Ans:C | P:93-Q:25-Ans:B

You may also enjoy...